Andrew Brodie Basics

LET'S DO GRAMMAR

FOR AGES 7–8

- Over 50 activities
- Regular progress tests
- Matched to the National Curriculum

with over **100** reward stickers

Andrew Brodie
An imprint of Bloomsbury Publishing Plc

50 Bedford Square
London
WC1B 3DP
UK

1385 Broadway
New York
NY 10018
USA

www.bloomsbury.com

ANDREW BRODIE is a trademark of Bloomsbury Publishing Plc

First published in Great Britain 2017

Copyright © Andrew Brodie, 2017

Cover and inside illustrations of Andrew Brodie and Pedro the panda © Nikalas Catlow, 2017
All other inside illustrations copyright © Cathy Hughes, 2017

Andrew Brodie has asserted his right under the Copyright, Designs and Patents Act, 1988,
to be identified as Author of this work.

A catalogue record for this book is available from the British Library.

ISBN
PB: 978-1-4729-4066-7
ePDF: 978-1-4729-4065-0

2 4 6 8 10 9 7 5 3 1

Designed and typeset by Marcus Duck Design
Printed and bound in China by Leo Paper Products

This book is produced using paper that is made from wood grown in managed,
sustainable forests. It is natural, renewable and recyclable. The logging and manufacturing
processes conform to the environmental regulations of the country of origin.

To find out more about our authors and books visit www.bloomsbury.com.
Here you will find extracts, author interviews, details of forthcoming events and the
option to sign up for our newsletters.

BLOOMSBURY

Notes for parents

What's in this book

This is the third in the series of *Andrew Brodie Basics: Let's Do Grammar* books. Each book features a clearly structured approach to developing and improving children's knowledge and use of grammar in their reading and writing as well as in their oral communication.

The National Curriculum states that children in Year 3 should learn appropriate terminology in relation to grammar and punctuation, including the following:
- consonant, consonant letter vowel, vowel letter
- word, word family, singular, plural, suffix, prefix, noun, noun phrase, adjective, verb, adverb, compound, conjunction, clause, preposition
- sentence, statement, question, exclamation, command, direct speech, paragraph
- present tense, present perfect tense, past tense
- punctuation: capital letter, full stop, question mark, exclamation mark*, apostrophe, speech marks, inverted commas.

*Note that in 2016 the Government stated that, in tests, pupils will only gain marks for exclamations that begin with *what* or *how*.

Children will learn to:

- extend their range of sentences with more than one clause by using a range of conjunctions, including *and*, *when*, *that*, *because*, *or*, *but*, *if* and *although*.

- use the present perfect in contrast to the past tense of verbs
- form nouns using a range of prefixes, e.g. *super*, *anti* and *auto*
- recognise word families
- use *a* or *an* correctly
- use conjunctions, adverbs and prepositions to express time and cause
- use the apostrophe for contraction and to mark singular possession
- punctuate direct speech, including writing dialogue for characters.

How you can help

Make sure your child is ready for their grammar practice and help them to enjoy it using the activities in this book. If necessary, read through each activity out loud, discussing it so that your child really understands what the writing means.

The answer section at the end of this book can be a useful teaching tool: ask your child to compare their responses to the ones shown. Their answers may not be identical but should include similar information. If your child has made mistakes, help them to learn from them. Remember that the speed at which your child progresses will vary from topic to topic.

Most importantly, enjoy the experience of working with your child and sharing the excitement of learning together.

Look out for...

Pedro the Panda, who will help your child understand what to focus on when working through the activities.

Brodie's Brain Boosters, which feature quick extra activities designed to make your child think, using the skills and knowledge they already have. Can they talk about their experiences using appropriate and interesting vocabulary?

Contents

Title	Focus	Page
Vowels and consonants	Letter types	4
Word families	Root words and derivatives	5
Using words in sentences	Correct punctuation	6
Finding nouns	Nouns in sentences	7
Singular and plural nouns	Identifying singular and plural	8
Making plural nouns from singular nouns	Adding s, es or ies	9
Progress Test 1		10
Verbs	Identifying and using verbs	11
Verbs ending with **ing**	Word search to find verbs	12
Present tense verbs	Present tense	13
Past tense verbs	Using **ed** to make the past tense	14
More past tense verbs	Unusual ways to make past tense	15
Sentences about the past	Using the past tense	16
Progress Test 2		17
Question sentences	Using question marks	18
Exclamation sentences	Using exclamation marks	19
Statement sentences	The most common type of sentence	20
Command sentences	Writing commands	21
Play script	Dialogue in script form	22
Speech marks	Using speech marks for dialogue	23
Progress Test 3		24
Adjectives	Identifying adjectives	25
Nouns and adjectives	Making noun phrases	26
Changing adjectives	Suffixes **er** and **est**	27
Strange adjectives	Non-standard adjectives	28
Adverbs	Identifying adverbs	29
A windy day	Finding adverbs in a story	30
Progress Test 4		31
Joining words	Conjunctions	32
More conjunctions	Joining sentences	33
Conjunctions search	Word search to find conjunctions	34
More conjunction practice	Using conjunctions	35
Prepositions	Finding and using prepositions	36
More prepositions	Using prepositions	37
Progress Test 5		38
Speech marks again	Using speech marks and commas	39
Speech verbs	Word search to find speech verbs	40
A lovely day	Apostrophes	41
A conversation	Punctuating a conversation	42
Past tense again	Past tense verbs	43
Present perfect tense	Introducing the present perfect	44
Progress Test 6		45
Answers		46

Vowels and consonants

Which letters can you say while keeping your mouth open?

You can say the letters a e i o and u with your mouth open. Try saying each one.

Now try saying the names and sounds of all the other letters of the alphabet.

a b c d e f g h i j k l m n o p q r s t u v w x y z

The letters a e i o and u are called vowels. The other letters are called consonants.

To form consonant sounds, you need to either put your lips together, move your tongue against the roof of your mouth or use your teeth.

Almost every word includes consonants and vowels.

The letter y is a special letter because it is a consonant but it sometimes works like a vowel.

Look at the word yellow. In this word the letter y is working as a consonant.

Look at the word dry. In this word the letter y is working as a vowel.

Here it is called a consonant letter vowel.

In the sentence below, underline all the vowels in red.

The quick brown fox jumps over the lazy dog.

Brodie's Brain Booster

What is special about the word rhythm?

Word families

Look at these words:
build building builder built rebuild rebuilt

All of the words are based on the root word build and are a word family.

Arrange the words below into word families.

moved movement household removal clear help rehouse house

cleared gardening remove clearance unclear helpful gardener unhelpful

housing helpless housed helpfully helper move garden housekeeper

house

hoaso hoase.
house

help

help
helpr

garden

move

move

clear

Using words in sentences

Choose one of the word families on page 5.

You are going to write some sentences. Remember, every sentence starts with a capital letter and ends with a full stop. Choose one of the word families from page 5, then write a sentence for each word in that family.

_____

_____

_____

_____

_____

_____

_____

_____

_____

_____

Brodie's
Brain Booster

Can you think of three words in the word family related to the root word **sign**?

Finding nouns

My friend is moving house.

Look at the sentence. It has two nouns, friend and house. Remember, a noun is a word that names something or someone.

Draw a ring around the nouns in each of the sentences below. Some of the sentences have three nouns.

The horse is running across the field.

The water is flowing quickly through the pipe.

The girl dived into the pool and swam to the shallow end.

Three birds landed on the roof of the house.

After breakfast, the boy was still hungry.

Write a sentence that includes the nouns children and school.

_____

_____

Brodie's Brain Booster

Do you remember what **singular** means?

Singular and plural nouns

Plural means more than one.

Look at this set of words:

van lorry car motorbike buses

The word **buses** is the **odd one out** because it is a **plural noun**.

Find the odd one out in each set of words. It will be a plural noun.

roof	floor	doors	tile	brick
girl	children	man	boy	woman
tables	chair	settee	stool	desk
football	matches	netball	rugby	hockey
cow	chicken	duck	sheep	horse

Find the odd one out in each set of words. It will be a singular noun.

glasses	screens	lamp	computers	telephones
guitar	violins	pianos	trumpets	drums
boots	shoes	sandals	flip-flop	slippers
wheels	engine	mirrors	gears	windscreens
room	kitchens	lounges	bathrooms	porches

Write a sentence that includes a singular noun and a plural noun.

_____

_____

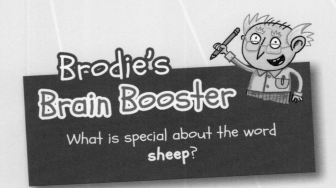

Brodie's Brain Booster

What is special about the word **sheep**?

Making plural nouns from singular nouns

The plural of bamboo is bamboo.

Some singular nouns can be changed into plural nouns just by adding **s**.

You need to add **es** to some nouns to make them plural.

Nouns that end with a **consonant then y** are made into plurals by taking off the **y** then adding **ies**.

Some singular nouns change a lot when they become plurals.

Write the plural noun for each of the singular nouns below.

ambulance _____

cloud _____

porch _____

couch _____

fairy _____

creature _____

knife _____

child _____

sheep _____

building _____

pony _____

accident _____

memory _____

county _____

wolf _____

Brodie's Brain Booster

What is the plural of **fish**?

Which letters are vowels?

| | | | | |

Which letters are consonants?

Which consonant can act as a vowel?

| |

Think of some words to go in this family.

survive

_____   _____

_____   _____

Choose two of the words from the survive word family. Write a sentence for each of the words you have chosen.

_____

_____

Find the plural noun for each of the singular nouns.

kitchen _____   lorry _____

leaf _____   woman _____

window _____

Verbs

Every sentence includes at least one verb.

The cat is chasing a mouse.

↑

This is a verb. It tells us what the cat is doing.

Be a verb detective. Draw a ring around each verb in the sentence below.

The mouse is climbing up the clock. The cat is watching.

The word climbing comes from the root word climb. The word watching comes from the root word watch. The suffix ing has been added to both of these root words.

Write a sentence using the word climb as a verb.

_____

_____

Write a sentence using the word watch as a verb.

_____

_____

Brodie's Brain Booster

Can you find all the nouns in the sentences, too?

Verbs ending with ing

Can you find the **ing** words? ✓

Look for the verbs ending with ing.

They may be written across, like this: **s u r f i n g**

They may be written down, like this: **d r e a m i n g**

There are six words to find. One has been done for you.

d	i	c	s	u	r	f	i	n	g
r	o	u	p	h	l	y	k	o	d
e	n	i	a	a	s	s	p	d	i
a	s	p	r	p	h	b	c	d	e
m	o	r	k	p	o	k	r	i	y
i	c	o	i	i	p	o	p	n	e
n	o	u	n	l	p	o	h	g	s
g	i	g	g	l	i	n	g	e	u
l	w	l	t	r	n	s	s	e	z
s	i	y	s	a	g	c	d	p	f

✓

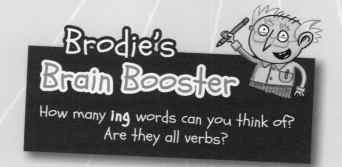

Brodie's
Brain Booster

How many **ing** words can you think of?
Are they all verbs?

Present tense verbs

**Things that are happening now are in the present.
Things that have already happened are in the past.**

Here are some sentences about things that are happening now.

**Jess lives in Birmingham. She is eating an apple.
She is drawing a picture.**

Every sentence includes at least one verb. Look at the verbs lives, eating and drawing. They are all in the present tense because they are all happening now. Did you notice that eating and drawing both have the word is before them, because we are using the pronoun she?

Here is another present tense sentence.

I am writing a sentence.

The verb writing has the word am before it, because we are using the pronoun I.

Write three sentences in the present tense.

_____

_____

_____

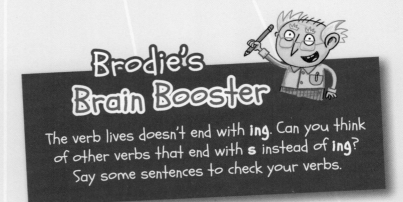

Brodie's Brain Booster

The verb lives doesn't end with **ing**. Can you think of other verbs that end with **s** instead of **ing**? Say some sentences to check your verbs.

Past tense verbs

I climbed a tree yesterday.

Things that have already happened are in the past.

Ted scored a goal.

Look at the verb scored. It is in the past tense because it is about something that has already happened.

Make the past tense verb from each of the verbs shown below. The first one has been done for you.

score	scored	look	
need		watch	
climb		float	
walk		park	
start		work	

Did you notice that all you had to do was to add the suffix ed?
Sometimes you have to double the final letter before adding the suffix ed

drop ➡ dropped

Make the past tense verb from each of the verbs shown here.

shop		snap	
hop		trap	
nip		spot	
step		plan	

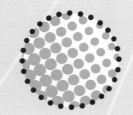

Brodie's Brain Booster

Can you think of any verbs where adding **ed** just won't work?

14

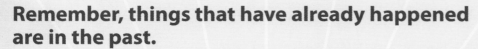

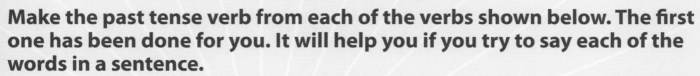

Some verbs change to the past tense in strange ways.

Remember, things that have already happened are in the past.

Ted slept well last night.

Look at the verb slept. It is in the past tense because it is about something that has already happened.

Make the past tense verb from each of the verbs shown below. The first one has been done for you. It will help you if you try to say each of the words in a sentence.

leave _____ *left* _____   build _____

come _____   give _____

sink _____   try _____

drive _____   bite _____

sleep _____   see _____

Some words are really strange. Look at these two sentences:

I go to school. ➡ I went to school.

The word go is in the present tense. It changes to went to become past tense.

Now try these.

do _____   break _____

begin _____   bring _____

sit _____   think _____

become _____   fall _____

Brodie's Brain Booster

Make up some sentences that include some unusual past tense verbs.

I can't remember what I did yesterday.

What did you do yesterday?

Write four sentences about what you did yesterday.

_____

_____

_____

_____

_____

_____

_____

Look at your sentences. Can you find the past tense verbs that you used? Write them down here.

_____

_____

_____

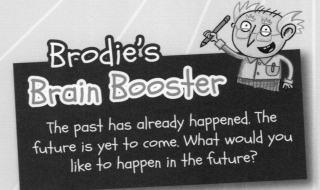

Brodie's Brain Booster

The past has already happened. The future is yet to come. What would you like to happen in the future?

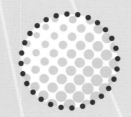

Progress Test 2

Be a verb detective. Draw a ring around the main verb in each sentence.

Isla is riding her bike.

Will is playing with a hula-hoop.

Make the past tense verb from each of the verbs shown here.

paint	______	want	______
offer	______	sweat	______
start	______	show	______
prevent	______	need	______

Now try these.

stop	______	decide	______
slip	______	feel	______
trip	______	see	______
step	______	hold	______
flap	______	keep	______
hug	______	know	______
grip	______	make	______
slot	______	take	______
draw	______	spend	______
fly	______	get	______
grow	______	sing	______

Question sentences

Imagine that two new children have just joined your class. Think about where they have come from. Perhaps they have moved house.

What questions could you ask them? Try to think of three good questions.

Don't forget to write a question mark at then end of your question sentences.

_____

_____

_____

_____

_____

_____

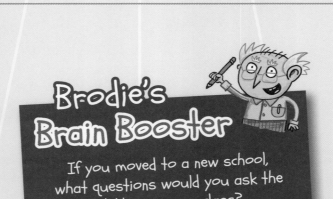

Brodie's Brain Booster

If you moved to a new school, what questions would you ask the children in your class?

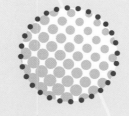

Exclamation sentences

An exclamation always ends with an exclamation mark.

How bright the moon is tonight!

What a beautiful moon is appearing!

Exclamations often start with How or What. The two sentences below have no punctuation. Rewrite them, remembering the capital letters and exclamation marks.

how cold it is today

_____

what a beautiful day it was yesterday

_____

Be careful because questions also often start with how or what. The two sentences below have no punctuation. Rewrite them, remembering the capital letters and question marks.

how are you feeling today

_____

what are you having for lunch

_____

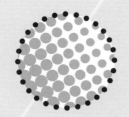

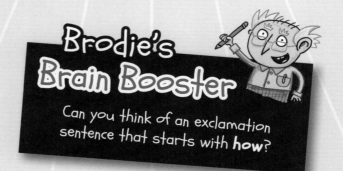

Brodie's Brain Booster

Can you think of an exclamation sentence that starts with **how**?

Statement sentences

Most sentences are statements.

I can see the moon shining brightly tonight.

The moon has brightened up the night so I can see clearly now.

Statements start with a capital letter and end with a full stop.

Write some statements about today. You could write about what you have done today or what you are going to do. You could write about today's weather. You could write about something special happening today.

_____

_____

_____

_____

_____

_____

Brodie's Brain Booster

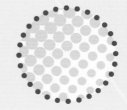

Write a statement about your favourite activity.

Command sentences

Lots of people tell me what to do.

Tidy my room.

The girl gave a command to the robot. She wanted her room tidied so she told the robot to do it for her.

Commands start with a capital letter and end with a full stop.

Write some commands for a robot. What would you like the robot to do for you?

_____

_____

_____

_____

_____

_____

Brodie's Brain Booster

Which people have given you commands today?

21

Play script

Tidy my room.

I will if you ask me nicely.

I've never been in a play – I'm too shy.

The girl gave a command to the robot and he made a reply. What they said to each other was shown in **speech bubbles**. We can also write what they said as a play script.

Girl: Tidy my room.

Robot: I will if you ask me nicely.

What do you think they said to each other next? Write some more lines of the play script.

_____

_____

_____

_____

_____

_____

Brodie's Brain Booster

A play script is a way of writing a story. It shows a conversation. Imagine a conversation on the telephone. Can you write this out as a script?

Speech marks

Tidy my room.

I like talking to other pandas.

I will if you ask me nicely.

The girl gave a command to the robot and he made a reply. What they said to each other was shown in speech bubbles. This is called direct speech.

"Tidy my room," said the girl.

"I will if you ask me nicely," replied the robot.

Look carefully at the first sentence.

"Tidy my room," said the girl.

These are called inverted commas or speech marks.

There is a comma before the closing speech marks.

Write a short conversation between two people, using speech marks correctly.

_____

_____

_____

_____

_____

Look at this short conversation between Mum and Jess.

Where have you been today?

I've been to gymnastics practice.

How energetic you are! Now get ready for lunch.

Identify each of the sentences. Write each one out under the correct sentence title.

Statement

_____

Question

_____

Exclamation

_____

Command

_____

Write out the first part of the conversation as direct speech.

_____

_____

_____

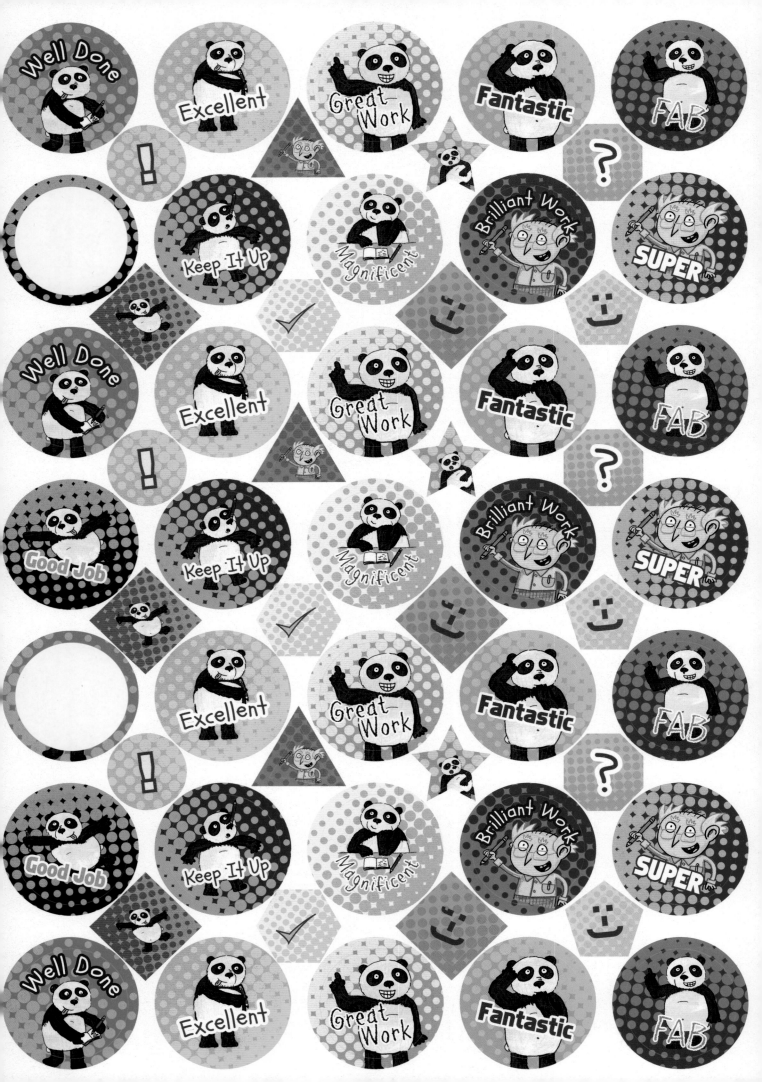

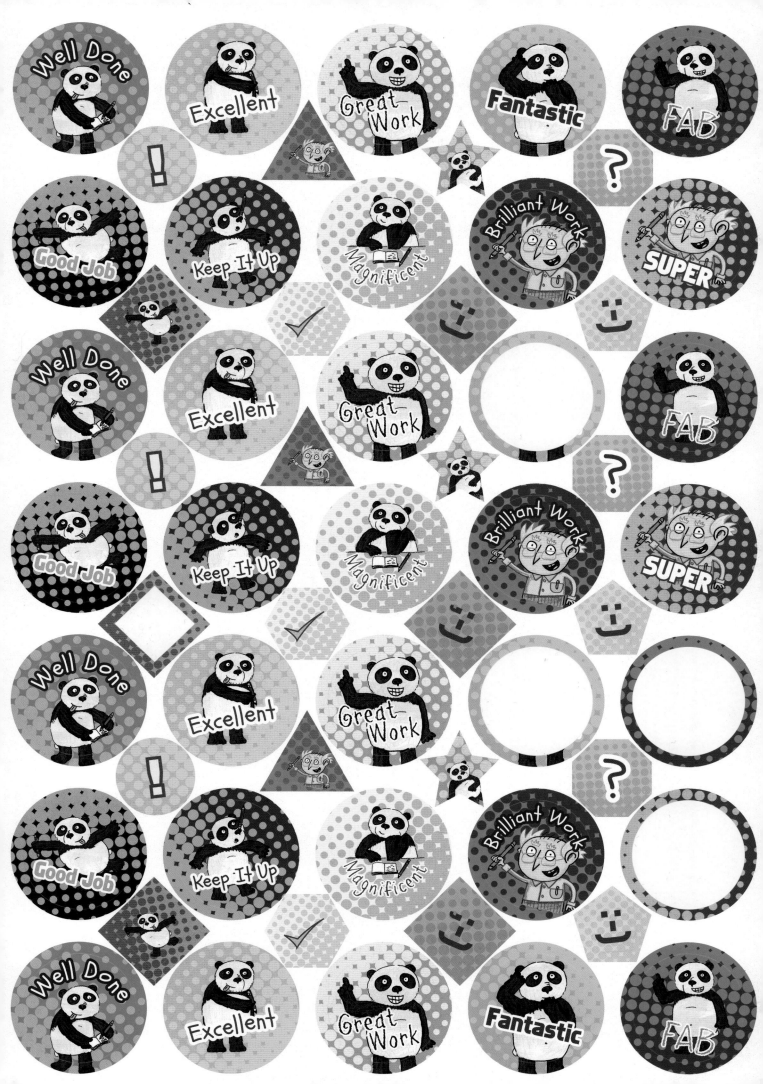

Adjectives

Adjectives are words that often go with nouns.

This is a noun.

This is a noun.

The little boy is riding on his new bike.

This is an adjective. It tells us something about the boy.

This is an adjective. It tells us something about the bike.

Draw a ring around the adjectives in each sentence below. Some of the sentences have only one adjective.

The little girl got lost in the big garden.

We wore smart clothes when we went to the party.

The tiny tree was planted in a huge pot.

Write two sentences about your school. Use at least one adjective in each sentence.

_____

_____

_____

Brodie's
Brain Booster

Look in your reading book. Pick any page. How many adjectives can you find?

Nouns and adjectives

Make some noun phrases by putting adjectives with nouns.

ADJECTIVE BOX:

happy   uncomfortable   wonderful

impossible   beautiful   unusual

NOUN BOX:

dream   people   clothes   views

task   vehicle   animals

Write some noun phrases using the words above. Each noun phrase needs an adjective with a noun. There are lots you can make. One has been done for you.

an unusual vehicle   an   an   an

anan   on an

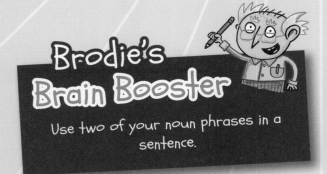

Brodie's Brain Booster

Use two of your noun phrases in a sentence.

Changing adjectives

You can change some adjectives by adding the suffixes **er** or **est**.

This is a small car.

This is a big car. It is bigger than the other one.

Look how **big** changes to **bigger** by adding the suffix er. In order to do this, the final g needed to be doubled.

Change these adjectives into new adjectives by adding the suffix er. Sometimes you will need to double the final letter first.

short _____   great _____

narrow _____   hot _____

bright _____   cool _____

This is the biggest of the cars.

Look how **big** changes to **biggest** by adding the suffix est. To add the suffix est an extra g had to be added.

Change these adjectives into new adjectives by adding the suffix est. Sometimes you will need to double the final letter first.

wide _____   cold _____

tall _____   dirty _____

dull _____   warm _____

Strange adjectives

Some adjectives are changed in strange ways.

Some adjectives are not changed by adding the suffixes er or est. They are changed differently.

This is a good present. This is a better present. This is the best present.

Look how the adjective big changes:

big ➡ bigger ➡ biggest

Look at how the adjective good changes:

good ➡ better ➡ best

Now try to change these adjectives.

bad ➡ [____] ➡ [____]

far ➡ [____] ➡ [____]

Some adjectives are changed by adding the words more or most.

This is an unusual hat.   This one is more unusual.   This one is the most unusual.

Write two sentences that change the adjective impressive.

This is an impressive jump.

_____

_____

Adverbs

Adverbs are words that often go with verbs.

The children are running down the road quickly.

↑   ↑

This is the verb. It tells us what the children are doing.   **This is the adverb. It tells how the children are doing it.**

The adverb is often right next to the verb, but sometimes it isn't.

Use a red pen and a blue pen. Use the red pen to draw a ring around each verb. Use the blue pen to draw a ring around each adverb.

The children are talking quietly.

Isla is colouring carefully.

The snow is falling heavily.

Here are some adverbs:

luckily   successfully   fantastically

Write a sentence using one of these adverbs.

_____

_____

Brodie's Brain Booster

Can you make an adverb from the adjective **wonderful**?

A windy day

I don't like windy days.

An adverb doesn't have to be next to a verb.

Can you find all the adverbs in this story?
Be careful, not all the sentences include an adverb.

The wind was blowing strongly. Jess held her new hat on her head carefully. A gust of wind surprised her suddenly. The hat blew quickly away. Jess chased after it.

Write the adverbs that you have found.

_____   _____

_____   _____

Write down the verbs in the story.

_____   _____

_____   _____

_____

Write down some of the nouns in the story.

_____   _____

_____

There is only one adjective. Can you find it?

_____

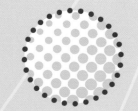

Brodie's
Brain Booster

Can you think of a short story
to write?

Use a red pen, a blue pen, a green pen and an orange pen. Use the red pen to draw a ring around each verb. Use the blue pen to draw a ring around each adverb. Use the green pen to draw a ring around each noun. Use the orange pen to draw a ring around each adjective.

Remember:
verb **red**
adverb **blue**
noun **green**
adjective **orange**

Ted ran quickly carrying the heavy branch.

The big cat was following the mouse quietly and carefully.

The teacher spoke crossly to the noisy children.

Make some adverbs from the adjectives below using the suffix ly.

careful _____   strong _____

harmful _____   attractive _____

Now try these.

unhappy _____   funny _____

steady _____   greedy _____

Joining words

Joining words are called conjunctions.

I went to the shop. I bought an ice cream.

We can join the two sentences together with the conjunction **and**.

I went to the shop and I bought an ice cream.

We now have one sentence made up of two clauses.

Here are three pairs of sentences. Join each pair of sentences together using the conjunction **and** or the conjunction **so**.

I climbed the hill. I saw a beautiful view.

_____

The weather is dry. We can play on the field.

_____

We drove to the seaside. We rushed on to the beach.

_____

Brodie's Brain Booster

Can you think of any other conjunctions?

I weant to paly in the gerd.

32

More conjunctions

I am very tired because I am working hard.

I am very tired. I am working hard.

We can join the two sentences together with the conjunctions because or but.

I am very tired **because** I am working hard.

or

I am very tired **but** I am working hard.

CONJUNCTION BOX:

and	because	but	if	so	that	or	although	when

Here are some pairs of sentences. Choose a conjunction to join each pair together.

I'm very busy today. I'm going to relax later.

_____

The sun is shining. It's quite chilly today.

_____

The car is very slow. It has a big engine.

_____

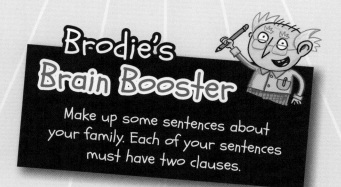

Brodie's Brain Booster

Make up some sentences about your family. Each of your sentences must have two clauses.

Conjunctions search

Can you find the conjunctions?

Look for the conjuctions.

They may be written across, like this: although

They may be written down, like this:
w
h
e
n

There are seven words to find. One has been done for you.

d	i	c	s	u	m	f	w	n	g
a	l	t	h	o	u	g	h	o	d
n	n	i	a	a	n	s	e	d	i
d	s	p	b	u	t	b	n	v	e
m	o	g	e	p	i	o	s	i	y
y	c	o	c	i	l	k	p	j	e
e	o	u	a	l	p	o	h	g	s
t	h	o	u	g	h	n	g	e	u
l	w	l	s	r	n	s	s	e	z
s	i	y	e	a	g	c	d	p	f

Brodie's
Brain Booster

Can you think of any other conjunctions?

34

More conjunction practice

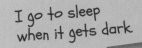

I go to sleep when it gets dark.

It gets dark. I go to sleep.

We can join the two sentences together with the conjunction when. It may be better to write the clauses in a different order when we do this.

I go to sleep when it gets dark.

Or it may be better to put the conjunction in a different place and to insert a comma.

When it gets dark, I go to sleep.

Here is a pair of sentences. Use the conjunction although to join them together. You may need to change the order of the clauses.

It's raining heavily. I'm going outside.

_____

You have made a sentence with two clauses. Make another sentence with the same two clauses but this time start the sentence with although. It would be a good idea to separate the clauses with a comma.

_____

Brodie's Brain Booster

Look in your reading book. Try to find some sentences that have more than one clause.

35

Prepositions

I like to sleep in a tree.

noun   noun

The panda is sleeping in a tree.

preposition

Prepositions are usually written before nouns. They usually link that noun to another word in the sentence. They often describe locations.

The panda is sleeping **in** a tree.

In this sentence the preposition **in** is before the noun **tree** and tells us about the location of the panda.

PREPOSITION BOX:

in   under   below   between   up   down   towards

Here are some sentences. Choose a preposition to fill each gap.

The coat cupboard is _____ the stairs.

There is a tree _____ the two houses.

The two children ran _____ the shop.

Brodie's Brain Booster

Look in your reading book. Try to find some prepositions.

36

More prepositions

Lots of words are prepositions.

PREPOSITION BOX:

up   down   on   at   over   after   by   between   towards   above   below

Here are some sentences. Choose a suitable preposition to fill each gap.

The plane flew _____ the clouds.

I looked _____ my own reflection.

The boy rolled _____ the hill.

We are going swimming _____ lunch.

The seagulls were skimming _____ the waves.

The coats are hanging _____ the front door.

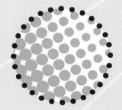

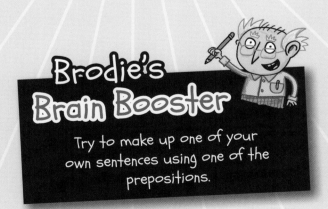

Brodie's Brain Booster

Try to make up one of your own sentences using one of the prepositions.

CONJUNCTION BOX:

and because but if so that or although when

Here are some pairs of sentences. Choose a conjunction to join each pair together.

Dinner is nearly ready. We can eat soon.

_____

Three birds came to the bird table. They didn't eat anything.

_____

Mum said I could have a treat. I have worked so hard.

_____

PREPOSITION BOX:

up down on off at over before after by

between towards above below

Here are some sentences. Choose a suitable preposition to fill each gap.

The ship was moving too quickly _____ the harbour.

The canoe raced _____ the rocks.

The children rushed _____ the stairs.

We can watch television _____ we've done our homework.

I had to climb _____ the wall to get my ball.

The shed is _____ the end of the garden.

Speech marks again

Do you
want to play
football?

Yes please.

Do you remember how to use speech marks?

The girl asked the boy a question and he replied.
What they said to each other is shown in speech bubbles above.
We can write what they said as direct speech**.**

"Do you want to play football?" asked the girl.

"Yes please," replied the boy.

Look carefully at the first sentence.

"Do you want to play football?" asked the girl.

These are called inverted commas **or** speech marks**.**

There is a question mark **before the closing speech marks.**

Look carefully at the second sentence.

"Yes please," replied the boy.

Inverted commas or speech marks.

The comma **is before the closing speech marks.**

Write a question and an answer as direct speech.

_____

_____

39

Speech verbs

Can you find the speech verbs?
They may be written across, like this: w h i s p e r e d
They may be written down, like this: a
s
k
e
d

There are seven words to find. One has been done for you.

w	h	i	s	p	e	r	e	d	g
a	l	t	h	o	u	e	h	o	d
f	n	i	o	a	n	p	e	d	i
d	s	p	u	u	t	l	n	c	e
m	o	r	t	p	i	i	r	a	y
a	c	o	e	i	l	e	p	l	e
s	a	i	d	l	p	d	h	l	s
k	h	o	u	g	h	n	g	e	u
e	x	c	l	a	i	m	e	d	z
d	i	y	e	a	g	c	d	p	f

Brodie's Brain Booster

Look in your reading book
What speech verbs can you find?

40

A lovely day

Is it a lovely day today?

What a lovely day!

It's not a lovely day. It's pouring with rain.

"What a lovely day!" commented Mum.

"It's not a lovely day. It's pouring with rain," replied Jess.

Look at this word: It's

This is an **apostrophe**.

It's is a short version of **It is**.

The apostrophe is used where the letter **i** has been missed out.

Write the short versions of the following pairs of words.
Use an apostrophe to shorten each pair.

do not _____   he is _____

did not _____   I am _____

she is _____   we are _____

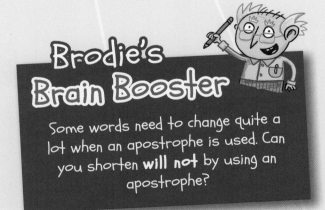

Brodie's Brain Booster

Some words need to change quite a lot when an apostrophe is used. Can you shorten **will not** by using an apostrophe?

41

A conversation

Create a conversation about going on holiday. Look back at the past three pages to remind yourself about how to use speech marks and speech verbs.

_____

_____

_____

_____

_____

_____

_____

_____

_____

_____

_____

_____

_____

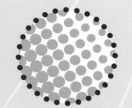

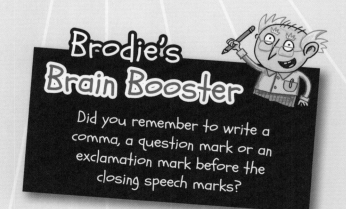

Brodie's Brain Booster

Did you remember to write a comma, a question mark or an exclamation mark before the closing speech marks?

Past tense again

Look at the short conversation to help you write your own.

"Where did Mum go yesterday?" asked Lena.

"She went to work," said Jakub.

Look at the verb **went**. It is in the past tense because it is about something that has already happened. The speech verbs **asked** and **said** are also in the past tense.

Write a sentence to answer the question in this conversation between Jasdeep and Tariq.

"What was the best thing you did last week?" asked Jasdeep.

_____

_____

What past tense verbs did you use?

_____

_____

Write a short conversation that includes a question and answer.

_____

_____

_____

_____

Brodie's
Brain Booster

Look in your reading book Can you find questions and answers?

Present perfect tense

> Dad has gone shopping.

"Where is Dad?" asked Lena.

"He has gone shopping," replied Jakub.

Look carefully at the second sentence.

"He has gone shopping," replied Jakub.

↑

This shows the present perfect tense.

The present perfect tense is used for something that started in the past but is still happening.

Underline the present perfect in the sentences below. One has been done for you.

I <u>have lived</u> in my house for four years.

It has been sunny all day.

The children have gone swimming.

Mum has bought a new car.

The post has arrived.

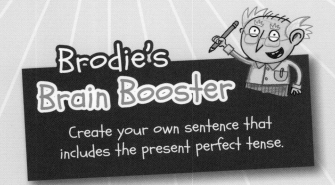

Brodie's Brain Booster

Create your own sentence that includes the present perfect tense.

Use an apostrophe to shorten these words.

they are _____   can not _____

we will _____   I would _____

you will _____   does not _____

I have _____

The punctuation is missing from the conversation below. Rewrite it with the correct punctuation.

how are you today asked the doctor

im very well thank you replied the old man

why have you come to see me asked the doctor

_____

_____

_____

Underline the present perfect in the sentences below.

I have finished my homework.

The builder has built a new house.

The party has started.

45

ANSWERS

Use the answers to check your child's progress but also to give prompts and ideas if they are needed. Note that sometimes your child's answer may not match the answer given here but could be just as good!

 p4

The quick brown fox jumps over the lazy dog.

Brain Booster

The word rhythm doesn't contain any vowels except for the consonant letter vowel y.

 p5

house: housing housed housekeeper household rehouse

help: helper helpful helpless helpfully unhelpful

garden: gardener gardening

clear: unclear cleared clearance

move: moved movement remove removal

 p6

Your child should choose one of the sets of words on page 5 and write a sentence to include each of the words. Check that each sentence starts with a capital letter and ends with a full stop.

Brain Booster

signed, signing, signature

 p7

horse, field, water, pipe, girl, pool, end, birds, roof, house, breakfast, boy.

Check your child's sentence includes the words children and school, and uses correct punctuation.

Brain Booster

Remind your child that singular refers to one thing.

 p8

doors children tables matches sheep lamp guitar flip-flop engine room

Check that your child's sentence includes a singular and plural noun.

Brain Booster

The word sheep is the same in both singular and plural form.

 p9

ambulances clouds porches couches fairies creatures knives children sheep buildings ponies accidents memories counties wolves

Brain Booster

fish or fishes – both are correct

Progress Test 1

How well does your child remember what they have practised?

a e i o u

b c d f g h j k l m n p q r s t v w x y z

y

survive: survived surviving survival survivor

Check your child's two sentences.

kitchens leaves windows lorries women

 p11

climbing, watching

Check your child's two sentences.

Brain Booster

cat mouse clock

 p12

d	i	c	s	u	r	f	i	n	g
r	o	u	p	h	l	y	k	o	d
e	n	i	a	a	s	s	p	d	i
a	s	p	r	p	h	b	c	d	e
m	o	r	k	p	o	k	r	i	y
i	c	o	i	i	p	o	p	n	e
n	o	u	n	l	p	o	h	g	s
g	i	g	g	l	i	n	g	e	u
l	w	l	t	r	n	s	s	e	z
s	i	y	s	a	g	c	d	p	f

Brain Booster

Help your child to think of words that end with ing.

 p13

Check that your child's three sentences are punctuated properly and that they are in the present tense.

Brain Booster

There are lots of examples: gives, shares, takes, builds, buys.

If your child uses them in spoken sentences they can tell whether the verbs 'work'.

 p14

needed climbed walked started looked watched floated parked worked

shopped hopped nipped stepped snapped trapped spotted planned

Brain Booster

There are lots of examples on page 15.

 p15

came sank drove slept built gave tried bit saw

did began sat became broke brought thought fell

Brain Booster

Help your child to compose some sentences.

p16

Check your child's sentences and help them to identify the past tense verbs.

Brain Booster

This is an opportunity for your child to talk about the future using appropriate vocabulary.

Progress Test 2

riding playing

painted offered started prevented wanted sweated showed needed

stopped slipped tripped stepped flapped hugged gripped slotted drew flew grew decided felt saw held kept knew made took spent got sang

p18

Check your child's sentences.

Brain Booster

Help your child to think of sensible questions using appropriate vocabulary.

p19

How cold it is today!
What a beautiful day it was yesterday!

How are you feeling today?
What are you having for lunch?

Brain Booster

Help your child to compose an exclamation sentence starting with how.

p20

Check your child's sentences.

Brain Booster

Help your child to compose a sentence about their favourite activity.

p21

Check that your child has written appropriate commands.

Brain Booster

Remind your child about commands that they have been given.

p22

Has your child written an appropriate play script?

Brain Booster

You could hold a telephone conversation with your child to give them ideas.

p23

The sentences should each have a capital letter at the start, a full stop at the end, speech marks for the spoken words and a comma, question mark or exclamation mark before the closing speech marks.

Progress Test 3

Statement: I've been to gymnastics practice.

Question: Where have you been today?

Exclamation: How energetic you are!

Command: Now get ready for lunch.

"Where have you been today?" asked Mum.

"I've been to gymnastics practice," replied Jess.

"How energetic you are! Now get ready for lunch," said Mum.

p25

little, big, smart, tiny, huge.

Check that your child's sentences include adjectives.

Brain Booster

Help your child to find adjectives in the reading book.

p26

There are lots of possibilities, eg. happy people, uncomfortable clothes, wonderful views, beautiful dream, an impossible task

Brain Booster

Can your child compose a suitable sentence?

p27

shorter narrower brighter greater hotter cooler

widest tallest dullest coldest dirtiest warmest

p28

bad worse worst
far further furthest (or farther farthest)

Your child should have written a sentence containing more impressive and a sentence containing most impressive.

Brain Booster

Examples: exciting, more exciting, most exciting, beautiful, more beautiful, most beautiful

p29

red rings (verbs): talking, colouring, falling blue rings (adverbs): quietly, carefully, heavily

Your child should compose a suitable sentence using one of the adverbs.

Brain Booster

wonderfully

p30

Adverbs: strongly, carefully, suddenly, quickly

Verbs: blowing, held, surprised, blew, chased

Nouns: wind, Jess, hat, head, gust, wind, hat, it (Don't be surprised if your child does not identify the proper noun Jess or the pronoun it. Many children will also not identify gust as a noun.)

Adjective: new

Brain Booster

Encourage your child to think of a set of sentences that tell a short story. They do not have to write the story down.

Progress Test 4

verbs (red): ran, carrying, following, spoke

adverbs (blue): quickly, quietly, carefully, crossly

nouns (green): Ted, branch, cat, mouse, teacher, children (Note that your child may not identify the proper noun Ted).

adjectives (orange): quickly, quietly, carefully, crossly

carefully harmfully strongly attractively unhappily steadily funnily greedily

p32

The weather is dry and we can play on the field. or The weather is dry so we can play on the field.

I climbed the hill and I saw a beautiful view. (Your child could choose to miss out the second I.)

We drove to the seaside and we rushed on to the beach. (Your child could choose to miss out the second we.)

Brain Booster

Examples: and, because, but, so, if, that, or, although, when

 p33

Help your child to choose an appropriate conjunction to join each pair of sentences.

Brain Booster

Talk about members of the family to help your child to compose some appropriate sentences.

 p34

d	i	c	s	u	m	f	w	n	g
a	l	t	h	o	u	g	h	o	d
n	n	i	a	a	n	s	e	d	i
d	s	p	b	u	t	b	n	v	e
m	o	g	e	p	i	o	s	i	y
y	c	o	c	i	l	k	p	j	e
e	o	u	a	l	p	o	h	g	s
t	h	o	u	g	h	n	g	e	u
l	w	l	s	r	n	s	s	e	z
s	i	y	e	a	g	c	d	p	f

Brain Booster

Examples: or, as, because, while.

 p35

I'm going outside although it's raining heavily.

Although it's raining heavily, I'm going outside.

Brain Booster

Help your child to find sentences with more than one clause.

 p36

under or below
between
towards

Brain Booster

Help your child to find some prepositions in their reading book.

 p37

over between towards above below at towards
down on over towards below at after
on over by between towards above on over by

Brain Booster

Can your child compose a suitable sentence?

 Progress Test 5

Note that your child may find suitable alternatives to those shown here.

Dinner is nearly ready so we can eat soon.

Three birds came to the bird table but they didn't eat anything.

Mum said I could have a treat because I have worked so hard.

The ship was moving too quickly towards the harbour.

The canoe raced between the rocks.

The children rushed up the stairs.

We can watch television after we've done our homework.

I had to climb over the wall to get my ball.

The shed is at the end of the garden.

p39

Your child should compose a question and an answer. Check that they have punctuated them correctly.

Brain Booster

Examples: said, shouted, whispered, answered, called.

 p40

w	h	i	s	p	e	r	e	d	g
a	l	t	h	o	u	e	h	o	d
z	n	i	o	a	n	p	e	d	i
d	s	p	u	u	t	l	n	c	e
m	o	r	t	p	i	i	r	a	y
a	c	o	e	i	l	e	p	l	e
s	a	i	d	l	p	d	h	l	s
k	h	o	u	g	h	n	g	e	u
e	x	c	l	a	i	m	e	d	z
d	i	y	e	a	g	c	d	p	f

Brain Booster

Can your child find speech verbs in the reading book?

 p41

don't didn't she's he's I'm we're

Brain Booster

won't

 p42

Check that your child has written appropriate sentences.

 p43

Your child should have written a correctly punctuated speech sentence ending with said Tariq or replied Tariq.

Brain Booster

Help your child to find questions and answers in their reading book.

 p44

has been
have gone swimming
has bought
has arrived

Brain Booster

Help your child to compose a suitable sentence.

Progress Test 6

they're we'll you'll I've can't I'd doesn't

"How are you today?" asked the doctor.

"I'm very well thank you," replied the old man.

"Why have you come to see me?" asked the doctor.

have finished
has built
has started